SLOW CARB DIET COOKBOOK

Effective Way To Nourish Your Body With Slow-Carb Recipes For A Quick Weight Loss

Lilian Veum

Disclaimer

This publication is designed to provide competent and reliable information regarding the subject covered. However, the views expressed in this publication are those of the author alone, and should not be taken as expert instruction or professional advice. The reader is responsible for his or her actions. The author hereby disclaims any responsibility or liability whatsoever that is incurred from the use or application of the contents of this publication by the purchaser of the reader. The purchaser or reader is hereby responsible for his or her actions.

ISBN:

Printed in the United States of America

Table of Contents

Introduction

Diets such as the ketogenic diet and slow-carb diet promote weight loss and health improvement using simple rules and whole, low-carb foods. The diets have both produced incredible weight loss results, some of which reached up to 100 pounds.

It is important to note, however, that the slow carb diet differs from other low-carb diets in many ways. For example, it incorporates some carb-rich foods and a cheat day at least once a week.

There are various nuances to consider before adding an "s" to low carb. While the approach may seem refreshingly simple, and it can be highly effective, there are several aspects to consider. Taking a closer look at this diet from the following standpoints will help you get a better idea of how it works for you.

Do well to read through to get all the details.

What is the Slow-Carb Diet?

Slow-carb diets follow five basic rules. Based on the principle of minimum effective dose (MED), this diet is very easy to follow. The smallest dose that produces the desired impact is what is meant by this definition.

To put it another way, it's about working the least amount of time to get maximum results. Consequently, this diet emphasizes following a few guidelines to maximize fat burn and weight loss.

You cannot eat from outside the allowed list of foods for six consecutive days while following the diet. Afterward, you get to eat anything you want one day a week.

You should limit your calorie intake during the diet days and try to consume no refined carbs, fruits, or high-calorie drinks.

There are only five basic food groups in the slow-carb diet: protein, vegetables, legumes, fat, and spices. The first three food groups are present in every meal, as well as small amounts of the last two.

Also included in the plan are recommendations for taking dietary supplements in order to speed up weight loss. You do not have to do this, however.

In similar fashion to the ketogenic diet, slow-carb diets support weight loss by consuming a lot of protein and very few carbs, since eating more protein will boost fat breakdown, increase feelings of fullness, and reduce fat storage.

5 Effective Rules of the Slow-Carb Diet

Slow Carb does not consider calories or macronutrients as part of your diet. Trying to follow Tim Ferris' five slow-carb diet rules to the letter will ensure our success.

#1: White Carbohydrates Are Prohibited - It is necessary to stay away from white carbs that are or can turn white in the first six days of the diet. It has been shown that white carbs can cause weight gain and are highly refined. There are several foods to avoid, including bread, white and brown rice, cereals, pasta, fried potatoes, and breaded foods.

#2: Repeat Select Meals Again and Again – The author states that there are hundreds of foods available, but only a few of them will keep you from gaining fat. The premise behind Rule #2 is that the participants will mix and match food from the selected group to make their meal plans and repeat them over and over again during the six days permitted.

It is safe for you to consume as much protein, lentils, and vegetables that are included in this special group as you like. Picking three or four slow-carb diet meals from the food list and repeating them is the recommended method of following the slow-carb diet. Keeping your meals simple is one of the key points you should keep in mind when preparing them.

#3: No-Calorie Drinks Are the New Norm – Depending on your choice of beverage, you can consume an astonishing amount of calories. Drinking them in large quantities will probably lead to weight gain. According to Rule #3, you should avoid drinking calorie-free beverages if you hope to lose weight.

Throughout the day, Ferris suggests drinking lots of water. Those interested in losing weight can drink as many no-calorie/low-calorie drinks as they want but should limit themselves to no more than 16 ounces of diet soft drinks per day. In addition to the fact that artificial sweeteners may cause weight gain, consumers should abstain from them. Dairy products, including soymilk, are off-limits on the Slow-Carb Diet, but red wine is permitted twice a day.

#4: Wave Goodbye to Fruit – According to Ferriss, avoiding fruit on the six days a week when the fruit is prohibited is the best approach. Due to the sugar in fruits, weight loss is slowed because you burn less fat and have more fat stored in your body.

In general, Rule #4 applies to all foods except tomatoes and avocados, the latter of which should be consumed in moderation. Ferriss suggests limiting yourself to one meal or one cup of coffee per day.

#5: You're Allowed One Cheat Day a Week – Having completed the sixth day of restriction, the Slow-Carb Diet allows you to indulge on one day where you will not be weighed down again. The cheat day does not count, nor do any of the others.

It is recommended that you cheat on Saturday. When he suggests that you gorge yourself on candy bars, chips and more delicious junk food, you get a big fat smile from him. It is possible to have a cheat day every day of the week, he says. It's also a good idea to begin the diet at least 5 days in advance of the cheat day of your choice. Accordingly, if you chose Monday following his decision, you should start your diet on Monday.

Tips to Achieve Optimum Results with Slow Carb

<u>Choosing the right foods and drinks to get the best results</u>

Vegetables and eggs should be part of your daily diet. As Tim found in his survey of slow-carb dieters, egg consumption and veggie consumption both had strong correlations with weight loss.

The opposite was true for alcohol consumption. This suggests that limiting alcohol consumption for slow-carb days and cheat days may be the most advisable approach.

Ensuring you get enough protein with each meal

Those following the slow-carb diet are advised to eat breakfast within an hour after waking up, preferably composed of at least 30 g of protein. As a result, satiety and blood sugar levels can be stabilized throughout the day.

A good rule of thumb is to space out meals approximately four hours apart after breakfast, so you will typically eat three to four meals per day. These meals should each contain a minimum of 20 grams of protein.

While it is recommended not to snack after a meal, you can have a small meal with just protein or just protein and vegetables if you are still hungry.

Don't Overeat Calorie-dense Foods

People tend to overeat healthy foods even though they are allowed on the slow-carb diet, such as nuts, nut butter, and hummus. In general, it is best to limit your consumption of food if you eat multiple servings in a single sitting.

Avoid Restaurant Carbs

Avoid carb-rich foods such as rice, pasta, potatoes, or fries at all costs.

Don't Worry about Calories

You should focus on eating slow-carbohydrate foods until you're satisfied rather than counting calories.

For a fuller feeling and to gain the most from your meals, chew well and eat slowly. Additionally, you will feel less hungry and your cravings will be diminished.

Take a Cold Shower to Start the Day

The slow-carb diet, combined with daily cold showers, is one lifestyle change Ferriss suggests. In an interesting finding, Tim discovered that those who tried taking cold showers but quit often also quit the diet.

Establish a Small Foundation and Build from there

You don't have to make all these lifestyle and diet changes at once if you feel overwhelmed. If you are experiencing difficulty losing weight, cut out all liquid sources of calories from your diet or start the day with a protein-rich breakfast (containing 30 grams of protein).

As you get comfortable with the changes, gradually introduce more of them into your daily routine.

Is it necessary for me to Take any Supplements?

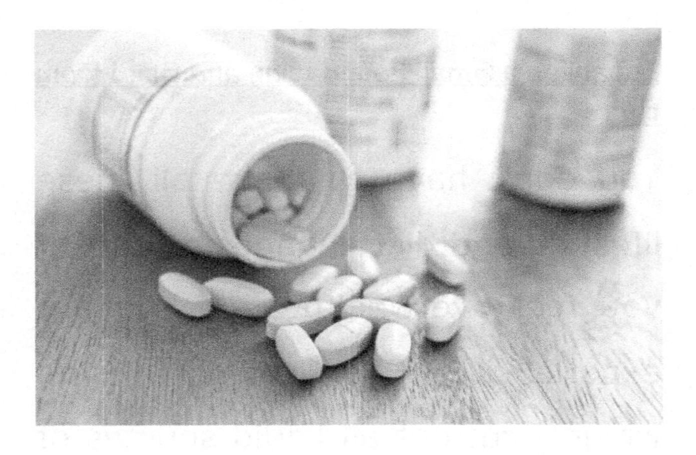

Due to the chances of losing excess water on the Slow-Carb Diet, it is advised that you replenish electrolytes with Magnesium and Calcium (1,000 mg daily, and 500 mg at night) to improve your sleep. Potassium supplements of 99 mg per meal are also recommended. Get a calcium and magnesium supplement to keep your body healthy.

There are some slow-carb options you can use in your diet if you prefer to get your electrolytes through whole foods. In terms of potassium, halibut and lima beans are good sources. If you want to eat magnesium, you should eat almonds and pine nuts. As a final note, tofu and spinach contain calcium. Ferriss takes Athletic Greens daily for overall health, although it's not essential for the Slow-Carb Diet.

Taking supplements known as the PAGG stack on The Slow-Carb Diet will maximize fat loss:

- Alpha-lipoic acid (Vitamin Shoppe ALA 100mg): 100-300 mg (Tim will take 300 mg with each meal, but he does not recommend this if you have acid reflux issues)
- Policosanol (Nature's Life Policosanol): 20-25 mg
- Garlic Extract (Allicin: 6000 Garlic 650mg)
- Green tea flavanols – decaffeinated with at least 325 mg

The weight loss supplement regimen recommended by Tim should be taken on six days a week, with one week off every two months. Here's the PAGG Stack supplement schedule.

Suggested Daily Schedule for Weight Loss Regimen:

- Pre-breakfast: green tea flavanols, garlic extract, and alpha-lipoic acid
- Pre-lunch: Flavonoids, garlic extract, and alpha-lipoic acid
- Pre-dinner: Green tea flavanols, garlic extract, and alpha-lipoic acid

- Pre-bedtime: Policosanol, arachidonic acid, and garlic extract

After and Before Results of the Slow-Carb Diet

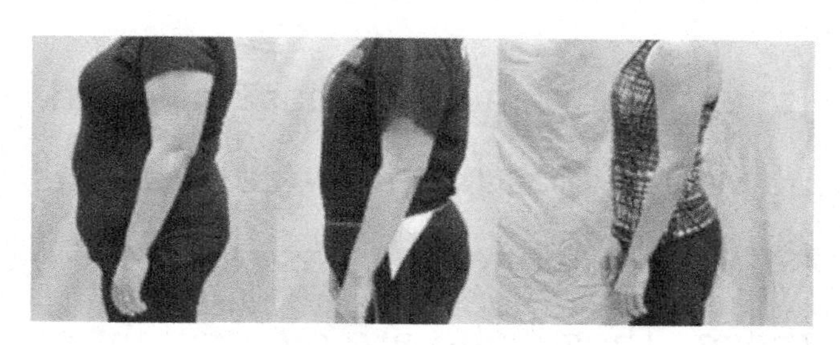

As a result of Tim's slow-carb survey, 84% of people who followed the diet for four weeks lost weight, and 14% of them lost at least 15 pounds.

As a result, 14 of every 100 people who followed the slow carb diet for four weeks lost over 3.75 pounds every week. It's incredible how much fat you're able to lose in such a short time!

It is important to bear in mind, however, that the slow carb diet is not the only one that has results like these. Those who are overweight or obese are more likely than not to lose fat after making significant dietary changes and sticking with them for four weeks.

Comparing and contrasting three different approaches, such as keto, paleo, and slow-carb, would be illuminating. All these methods, even though they have different principles and rules, have proven to be effective in helping people lose fat.

To achieve amazing results, you don't have to eat like a caveman, follow slow-carb rules, or restrict net carbs. All of them work in much the same way: by reducing energy intake sufficiently to cause fat loss.

All weight-loss strategies are based on such a common principle, whether they are ketogenic or vegan diets, low-carb diets or zero-carb diets.

However, you won't be able to stick to a diet if you are not aware of what works and what doesn't. A sustainable and healthy diet is crucial to achieving the results you desire and maintaining them long-term.

To determine what you should try first, determine what fits your lifestyle, health goals, and preferences. Let's look at the potential downsides of the slow carb diet to decide if this is something you want to try.

Potential Downsides and Criticisms of Slow-Carb

Even though the slow-carb approach has the potential for incredible results, it contains many methodological flaws that could mislead us and cause us more weight loss and health issues than necessary. As long as we address these potential downsides, we can help you find a diet that meets your needs.

In my opinion, the slow carb diet has a number of glaring vulnerabilities:

There are some faulty premises in the rules

Although many of us can achieve sustainable body transformations by following the slow-carb rules, that doesn't mean that those rules are good or justified. Moreover, the concept of universally slow-digesting/slow-burning carbs (which is based on the name "slow-carb diet") does not appear to be supported by research.

It has been found that the glycemic response to carb-rich foods varies greatly from person to person (even from meal to meal). As a result, someone with high blood sugar and insulin levels may still experience a significant spike after eating a 100% slow carb meal, which is precisely what Ferriss was trying to prevent with his slow-carb rules.

As a result, it's not possible or necessary to track one's glycemic response after every meal to lose fat and get healthier. To lose weight healthily and sustainably, you should focus on a lifestyle that allows you to consume fewer calories, burn fat stored inside your body, and improve overall health without feeling deprived.

Those who meet these criteria might benefit from a slow carb diet.

If you are having trouble following a slow-digesting carb diet, try not to let the concept of "slow-digesting carbohydrates" keep you from finding a healthier diet.

Unhealthy eating habits and poor mental health can be a consequence of cheat days

It is common for simple rule-based approaches such as slow-carb to lead to an unhealthy obsession with food choices, which in turn can lead to a loss of mental health.

It is enough for some of us to perpetually daydream about those cheat days, trigger bingeing behaviours, and limit the enjoyment of slow-carb meal days just by knowing we have one each week.

A cheat meal can also cause a massive drop in energy levels, inflammation, and water retention, which is another issue we struggle with. Those who have struggled with body dysmorphia, eating disorders, or depression in the past should consider this.

It is still possible to gain fat while losing weight through cheat meals

Issuing a cheat day would be counterproductive if the increase in calories on your slow-carb diet had not resulted in enough fat loss. Unfortunately, not everyone will experience those same benefits if they follow this type of eating plan.

Depending on the person, one cheat day could be all that is required to regain the fat lost during the week. Your chances of experiencing this will increase even more if you eat mostly processed food, drink sugary beverages, and consume alcohol during your cheat day.

You may find that your circumference measurements and weight are higher than expected after a cheat day due to the increased water retention. As a result, you should check your results every four to six weeks, on the same day of the week.

Nutrient deficiencies can result from eating the same meals every day

If you follow rule #2 exactly, you may experience several mineral and vitamin deficiencies after a few months. Therefore, you must monitor your health and well-being as with any major dietary change. A change in diet or supplementation can often easily remedy unexpected symptoms or health concerns.

How to Decide if Slow-Carb is Right for you

By understanding what the benefits and downsides of this approach could be, you will be able to make an informed decision.

A slow-carb diet would look a lot like something you haven't been successful with in the past, so there is no reason to assume that adding the "slow carb" label will make it more effective. Perhaps you would be better off following a more consistent low-carb diet like a keto diet.

You need to experiment with a slow carb diet for about 2-3 months if you haven't tried anything like it yet.

Keep track of your physical and mental health at all times during the process. You should see a positive trend in your body composition, your mental health, and your blood work after each month.

Dietary Guidelines for Slow-Carb Eating

To develop a slow-carb diet, here are several suggestions:

- Low-carb vegetables — crucifers, leafy greens
- Legumes — beans of any type including lentils, chickpeas, and peanuts

- Animal Protein — such as egg whites, fish, shellfish, poultry and organ meats
- And, of course, 1-2 glasses of red wine (I will recommend Malbec)
- Herbs and spicy herbs — cumin, mint, curry, and oregano.
- Nuts and seeds — flax seeds, avocados, macadamias, chia seeds, pecans, cashews, walnuts, etc.
- Others — bone broth, tomatoes, coconut milk, vinegar, soy sauce, hummus and low-carb condiments

- Fats/Oils — ghee, grass-fed butter, coconut oil, nut butter, extra virgin olive oil and macadamia oil

Foods to Avoid on a Slow-Carb Diet:

- Dairy — yogurt, cheese, cream, etc
- Sugar – agave, honey, maple syrup, etc
- Fruit – apples, oranges, bananas, berries, etc
- Grains – rice, wheat, corn, oats, cereal etc
- Starchy vegetables – yams, potatoes, beets, etc

- Drinks with calories — alcohol, soda, smoothies, juice etc

In this case, grass-fed butter is the only exception

Last but not least, here is a list of foods that several slow-carb dieters have been able to incorporate back into their diets:

- Carrots
- Jicama
- Yam
- Acorn Squash
- Beets
- Berries
- Sugar-free cottage cheese

- Parmesan cheese and other hard cheeses
- Parsnips
- Butternut Squash
- Sweet Potato
- Pumpkin
- Squash

To achieve the best slow carb diet results, it is advisable to stick to the slow carb food list listed above.

Keto Crispy Ginger Mackerel Lunch Bowl

Vegetables, protein, healthy fats, beneficial micronutrients, and flavor are all in this slow-carb bowl. The recipe can be followed as-is or you can whip up a concoction of your own using this bowl as a guide.

If you have canned salmon, tuna, or sardines on hand, just experiment with them!

Mackerel has captured my heart! I only recently became interested in this fish, which is an oily fish consumed throughout the world. It contains a lot of omega-3 fatty acids, which I always strive to consume more of.

With this recipe, you can turn mackerel into an impressive meal with a wide variety of flavors. Ginger, lemon, and coconut aminos are mixed into a marinade before roasting the fish in the oven. Sun-dried tomatoes, broccoli, and peppers make up the bowl's base.

Afterwards, roasted almonds and guacamole finish everything off.

Keto Crispy Ginger Mackerel Lunch Bowl	Calories	Fats(g)	Carbs(g)	Fiber(g)	Net Carbs(g)	Protein(g)
1 tablespoon butter	102	12	0	0	0	0.1
1/3 cup diced red bell pepper	13	0.1	3	0.5	2.5	0.4
1 tablespoon lemon juice	2.6	0	0.8	0.1	0.7	0.1
3 tablespoons olive oil	358	41	0	0	0	0
1 tablespoon coconut aminos	12	0	3	0	3	0
2 (8-ounce) boneless mackerel fillets	461	31	0	0	0	42
1 ½ cups broccoli	82	1	11	7.7	3.3	5.6
½ small yellow onion	13	0.1	3	0.4	2.4	0.4
2 small sun-dried tomatoes	10	0.1	2.2	0.5	1.7	0.6
1-ounce almonds	170	15	6	3.1	2.9	5.9
4 tablespoons mashed avocado	70	6.4	3.7	2.9	0.8	0.9
1 tablespoon grated ginger	5.5	0.1	1.2	0.1	1.1	0.1
Totals	1299.1	106.8	33.9	15.3	18.4	56.1
Per Serving(/2)	649.55	53.4	16.95	7.65	9.2	28.05

The Preparation

Lunch bowl:

- 4 tablespoons mashed avocado
- ½ small yellow onion
- 1 tablespoon butter
- 1/3 cup diced red bell pepper

- 2 (8-ounce) boneless mackerel fillets
- 1ounce almonds
- 1 ½ cups broccoli
- 2 small sun-dried tomatoes, chopped

Marinade:

- Salt and pepper, to taste
- 1 tablespoon lemon juice
- 3 tablespoons olive oil
- 1 tablespoon coconut aminos
- 1 tablespoon grated ginger

The Execution

- Pre-heat the oven to 400 degrees Fahrenheit. Use parchment paper or foil to line a baking tray. Add a little salt and pepper along with the grated ginger, lemon juice, olive oil, and coconut aminos. Apply half of the marinade to the mackerel fillets.

- With the skin side facing up, place the fish fillets on the baking sheet. The skin should be crispy after 12-15 minutes of roasting.
- Almonds should be spread out on a separate baking sheet. Bake for 5-6 minutes or until they are browned. Before chopping, remove from the oven and let cool.

- To make the broccoli mush-free, gently steam it for a few minutes until the broccoli has softened but not become mushy. Cut it into rough pieces.
- Add the butter to a pan and heat it over medium heat until it melts completely. The onion and pepper should be soft after they have been fried.
- After adding the broccoli and sun-dried tomatoes, cook until warmed.
- Combine the rest of the dressing with the roasted almonds after turning off the

heat. The avocado should be served with it.

Bacon Wrapped Asparagus with Garlic Aioli

The asparagus wrapped in bacon can be served to visitors (or to yourself) with no regrets. Asparagus and bacon combine their bitter and distinct flavors in a delicious way to create a tasty and filling dish. Topping it all off with a smooth and garlicky aioli is a recipe for success. Even though I'm not a huge asparagus fan, when they're cooked right and covered in bacon, I'll eat it any day!

My favorite way to add fat to a dish that lacks fat is to make easy sauces that go well with it. Garlic aioli is simple (and I mean it!) and it will do the trick here. Making aioli can be a bit tedious since you are essentially making your mayonnaise, so why not reduce the work by using one of the easy options: store-bought or homemade mayonnaise? It's a quick way to add a ton of flavor (and lots of fat) to your food. In the meantime, compliment the taste profiles of everything you have worked so hard to create.

If you finish this dish, you'll have half of the garlic aioli leftover, which can be used as a sauce with other meats or served over salads. When you're finished cooking the asparagus, there will still be bacon fat and olive oil in the baking pan, which is why you're left with half. The result is an extremely rich and fattening sauce - drowning out all other flavors with the flavor of bacon fat. If you use only half the aioli recipe for this, you'll end up with a very fattening and rich-tasting sauce. I wasn't aiming for that flavor profile, even though sometimes that can be a good thing.

Bacon Wrapped Asparagus with Garlic Aioli	Calories	Fats(g)	Carbs(g)	Fiber(g)	Net Carbs(g)	Protein(g)
¼ cup mayonnaise	390.3	42.57	0.69	0	0.69	1.74
2 tablespoons olive oil	239	27	0	0	0	0
1 large egg yolk	55	4.51	0.61	0	0.61	2.7
2 teaspoons fresh lemon juice	2	0.02	0.69	0	0.69	0.04
2 teaspoons minced garlic	4	0.01	0.93	0.1	0.83	0.18
1 ½ pounds asparagus	136	0.82	26.38	14.3	12.08	14.96
6 slices bacon	701	66.68	2.15	0	2.15	21.2
Totals	1527.3	141.61	31.45	14.4	17.05	40.82
Per Serving(/3)	509.1	47.2	10.48	4.8	5.68	13.61

The Preparation

- 1 large egg yolk
- 1 ½ pounds asparagus
- 2 teaspoons fresh lemon juice
- Rendered bacon fat & olive oil
- 2 tablespoons olive oil
- Salt, pepper, and red chili flakes to taste
- Simple Garlic Aioli

- ¼ cup mayonnaise
- Bacon Wrapped Asparagus
- 6 slices bacon
- 2 teaspoons minced garlic
- ¼ teaspoon kosher salt

The Execution

- Preheat the oven to 400 degrees Fahrenheit.
- Make six bundles of asparagus (each bundle contains about 11 stalks). Remove 1 inch of the asparagus bottom if necessary.
- As you wrap each bundle of stems, start on the bottom and work your way up.

- Then wrap the foil around the asparagus and bake it. To season, drizzle olive oil, salt, pepper, and red chili flakes.
- Broil the bacon for an additional 2-5 minutes so that it is crispy after baking.
- Adding garlic, mayo, egg yolk, baked-on fat and salt to the mixture is a great way to flavor it.
- Blend the aioli well until it is smooth.

Classic Bacon and Eggs

With eggs being associated with better results on a slow carbohydrate diet, this recipe makes a great staple to add to your weekly menu. Tomatoes are not to be forgotten! Your meal will taste even better and offer even more health benefits if you add them.

As an alternative to two eggs, simply have three and follow tip **#2** (a minimum of 30 grams of protein within 60 minutes of walking).

Here is how we make bacon & eggs - the most classic keto breakfast! In addition to cooking the bacon, we enjoy frying up the eggs in bacon fat. You can get this at your favorite fast-food joint, too, with fresh parsley and cherry tomatoes.

Breakfasts like bacon and eggs help you stay satiated throughout the day since it's a hearty breakfast.

<u>Preparation</u>

Classic Bacon and Eggs	Calories	Fats(g)	Carbs(g)	Fiber(g)	Net Carbs(g)	Protein(g)
1/4 cup chopped parsley	5.4	0.1	0.9	0.5	0.4	0.5
8 large eggs	663	50	2.4	0	2.4	48
5 ounces sliced bacon	572	38	2.9	0	2.9	50
Per Serving(/4)	322.35	22.15	4.3	0.95	3.1	25.23
16 cherry tomatoes	49	0.5	11	3.3	6.7	2.4
Totals	1289.4	88.6	17.2	3.8	12.4	100.9

- Yield: 4 servings
- Serving Size: 1/4 recipe
- Calories per serving: 322.35
- Fat per serving: 22.15

<u>The Execution</u>

- On medium-high heat, fry the bacon slices until they are crispy. The bacon fat should remain in the pan while you set the bacon aside.
- Open the eggs and place them in the hot bacon grease. You can prepare them as you wish.

- Add salt and pepper to the eggs, and then top with the bacon. Place the cherry tomatoes on the hot skillet for a few minutes until they are roasted.
- Garnish with the parsley when serving the tomatoes with the bacon and eggs.

Four servings of Classic Bacon and Eggs are made from this recipe. This recipe comes out to 322.35 calories, 22.15 grams of fat, 3.1 grams of carbs, and 24.23 grams of protein per serving.

Cabbage and Bacon One-Pan Keto Bowl

A slow-carb bowl sounds good to you, but are you ambivalent about fish? Make cabbage and bacon with this simple, fast, and delicious recipe. Three ingredients and one pan are all that you need: bacon, cabbage, and butter.

A good side dish to a steak or pork chop recipe can also be made with this recipe.

Sauteed cabbage with bacon and butter makes a delicious one-pan meal. One of the best things about this dish is that it is so easy to memorize that you can make it again and again. It is one of the staples of the keto diet!

You can portion up this dish into smaller servings if you wish to serve it as a side dish. The dish would be perfect with our smothered Instant Pot pork chops, or our seared ribeye steak. It keeps well enough to serve as a meal prepping recipe and would make a great lunchbox addition. Alternatively, you can make this recipe using ground sausage instead.

Preparation

One-Pan Cabbage and Bacon Keto Bowl	Calories	Fat(g)	Carbs(g)	Fiber(g)	Net Carbs(g)	Protein(g)
2.00 tablespoon butter	203	23	0	0	0	0.2
6.00 ounce bacon	907	79.4	0	0	0	45.4
16.00 ounce green cabbage	113	0.3	26.3	11.3	15	5.8
Totals	1223	102.7	26.3	11.3	15	51.4
Per Serving(/2)	611.74	51.33	13.15	5.65	7.5	25.68

- Yield: 2 servings
- Serving Size: 1/2 recipe
- Calories per serving: 611.74
- Fat per serving: 51.33

The Execution

- Bacon and cabbage should be chopped into small, bite-sized pieces.

- In a medium pan, cook the bacon until it has been rendered and is crispy.
- Then add the cabbage, butter, salt, and pepper. The cabbage should be golden brown and soft when finished frying.
- Serve with pan drippings in a bowl.

Two servings of One-Pan Cabbage and Bacon Keto Bowl result from this. This meal contains 611.74 calories, 51.33 grams of fat, 7.5 grams of net carbohydrates, and 25.68 grams of protein per serving.

Pesto Avocado Walnut and Zucchini Ribbons

Thankfully, zucchini noodles have continued to improve in both taste and convenience, making them the holy grail of ketogenic pasta dinners. It is often difficult to make "zoodles" without a fancy machine that makes zucchini noodles. What is the solution? There's nothing like a Zucchini ribbon!

Use a standard vegetable peeler and some elbow grease to create faux pasta ribbons from your most popular summer veggies. Impress your friends with your fancy cooking skills! Is there anything better?

Pesto is a sauce that is made of basil, pine nuts, and tons of olive oil. Keto pasta dressing is made with less oil so that it is even more keto-friendly. Plus, if you are anything like me and spend your hard-earned (keto) dough on avocados, you certainly don't want to spend that dough on pine nuts at $9 for a small container. This flavorful dish is perfectly enhanced by the subtle nutty flavor of walnuts.

Zucchini Ribbons with Avocado Walnut Pesto	Calories	Fats(g)	Carbs(g)	Fiber(g)	Net Carbs(g)	Protein(g)
½ cup water, if needed*	0	0	0	0	0	0
1 tablespoon olive oil	119	13.5	0	0	0	0
5-6 fresh (2.5 g) basil leaves to garnish	1	0.02	0.07	0	0.07	0.08
½ large lemon, juice	5	0.06	1.66	0.1	1.56	0.08
leaves	6	0.15	0.64	0.4	0.24	0.76
3 medium (588 g) zucchini	100	1.88	18.29	5.9	12.39	7.11
½ teaspoon salt	0	0	0	0	0	0
½ large (68 g) avocado	114	10.48	5.88	4.6	1.28	1.33
¼ cup (29.25 g) walnuts chopped	191	19.07	4.01	2	2.01	4.45
2 cloves (6 g) garlic,peeled	9	0.03	1.98	0.1	1.88	0.38
¼ cup (25 g) grated Parmesan cheese	106	6.96	3.48	0	3.48	7.11
Totals	651	52.15	36.01	13.1	22.91	21.3
Per Serving(/2)	325.5	26.08	18.01	6.55	11.46	10.65

The Preparation

Avocado Walnut Pesto

- ¼ cup grated Parmesan cheese
- ½ cup water, if needed
- ½ large avocado
- 2 cloves garlic, peeled
- ½ large lemon

- 1 cup fresh basil leaves
- ¼ cup walnuts

Zucchini Ribbons

- ½ teaspoon salt
- 3 medium zucchini

Other

- 5-6 fresh basil leaves to garnish
- 1 tablespoon olive oil
- Salt and pepper to taste
- Optional: Italian seasoning

<u>The Execution</u>

- Using a vegetable peeler or mandolin slicer, cut the zucchini into delicate ribbons, stopping at the seeds to stop peeling.

- Salt the ribbons in a colander and place them in a bowl. Prepare avocado pesto as you stand.
- Bring the avocado-walnut pesto ingredients together. This includes basil, avocado, lemon, walnuts, garlic and cheese.
- The sauce should be smooth after adding all of the ingredients to the food processor. Depending on the consistency of the sauce, add water.

- One tablespoon of olive oil should be added to a skillet and brought to medium heat.
- Slice the zucchini into ribbons and saute for 3-5 minutes, or until they are beginning to soften. Take out of the heat.
- Gently toss zucchini ribbons with pesto.
- Serve with two ribbons of vegetable ribbons beautifully swirled. Serve with grated Parmesan cheese and fresh basil.

Keto Breakfast Bowl

We've taken the traditional Filipino tapsilog recipe and turned it into a keto version with cauliflower rice! Sweet and savory, this keto recipe makes a great protein breakfast.

If you have some extra time for cooking a hearty family breakfast, you might try out this recipe. It's the perfect brunch you can enjoy through dinner. Due to the overnight marinating requirement, you will have to plan far in advance.

Keto Breakfast Bowl	Calories	Fats(g)	Carbs(g)	Fiber(g)	Net Carbs(g)	Protein(g)
garlic, minced	27	0.1	6	0.4	5.6	1.1
Calamansi juice	13	0	3.3	0	3.3	0
1 cup coconut oil	1945	216	0	0	0	0
rice	113	1.3	23	9.1	13.9	8.7
4 large eggs	286	19	1.4	0	1.4	25
powder	31	0.1	6.8	0.8	6	1.5
granulated erythritol	0	0	0	0	0	0
1 pound beef sirloin	1101.7	64.7	0	0	0	122.3
¼ cup soy sauce	34	0.4	3.1	0.5	2.6	5.2
Totals	3550.7	301.6	43.6	10.8	32.8	163.8
Per Serving(/4)	887.68	75.4	10.9	2.7	8.2	40.95

The Preparation

- ¼ cup soy sauce
- 3 teaspoons garlic powder
- 1 pound beef sirloin
- 1 pound cauliflower rice
- 4 large eggs

- 6 medium cloves garlic, minced
- 1/8 cup Calamansi juice
- 1 tablespoon granulated erythritol
- 1 cup coconut oil

The Execution

- Mix together soy, sweetener, citrus, garlic, garlic powder, pepper and salt. Once the salt and sweetener are dissolved, stir the mixture immediately.
- Put the beef in the Ziploc bag and pour the marinade over it. To cure, place in the refrigerator overnight.

- After the meat has marinated, remove it from the marinade. Your stove should be preheated before you start cooking. Put coconut oil on the pan.
- Fry the hamburger slices in one layer, turning them on the sides once, until all of the liquid is absorbed.
- The beef should be removed from the pan. Before slicing the beef into strips, allow it to cool.
- Continue cooking the parmesan and garlic in the remaining coconut oil.

- Mix the salt, garlic powder, and minced garlic into the oil. Stir-fry until aromatic.
- Toss evenly with cauliflower rice.
- Make sure the meat is almost dry when tender. Then season with the rest of the garlic powder and black pepper.
- Separately, cook eggs until they reach the desired consistency.
- With cauliflower rice, eggs, and steak strips and favorite toppings, remove from pans.

NOTES

NOTES

NOTES

Made in the USA
Monee, IL
22 February 2024

53942255R00046